First edition : 2021
ISBN : 978-1-3999-0709-5

Layout by Cat Houston @Myriad Pro Publishing

This book belongs to:

_____

_____

_____

_____

_____

Buttony first arrived at a time in our lives when we felt totally alone in what we were going through. We didn't have the words to explain to our eldest daughter what was happening with her baby sister, who at just two days old was having emergency surgery to form a stoma. But then along came a bear with a button and a bag, looking like our baby, and snuggled itself into our daughters' hearts. Buttony was by their side during long, lonely hospital stays. When we did stoma bag changes, her sister did Buttony's too. And when we were finally ready to come home, Buttony was right there waiting for us all. Many years later, words can not describe what a comfort Buttony has been to all of us. Having a playful way to explore such a serious condition has helped us all adjust to life with a stoma and has given our children a way to express themselves about this complicated issue. Even now after our daughter's stoma has been reversed, Buttony still holds a special place in our family. Such a special bear deserves their own story, don't you think?

I wrote this story to give Buttony a voice, as he has given a voice to so many families searching for a way to talk to their children about stomas. We are often taught from a young age not to talk about poo in polite company, and my hope for this book is that it normalises the conversation, particularly for families affected by stomas. The special closeness of story time is the perfect opportunity to introduce more challenging topics, and in Buttony kids will find a proud yet playful role model who shows kids not to be embarrassed or ashamed of this condition, and the comfort that comes from knowing you are not alone.

from the author, Kathryn Bradley

For Emily, Sophie
and all the staff on
Ward D35

A Friend
Just Like Me

A Poem by
Kathryn Bradley

Illustrated by
Georgina Croll

Hello, new friend. My name's Buttony.

Will you hear my story and look after me?

I've searched high...

and low...

Across the desert...

Through the wind...

rain...

and snow...

to find a friend just like me.

I'm special, you see,
not quite like the rest,

but be friends with me and I'll love you best.

When I was small,
I had a poorly tummy.

I couldn't eat at all
and was in hospital
with Mummy.

A doctor then came, said she knew what to do:

"A stoma's our aim,
it'll change
how you poo!"

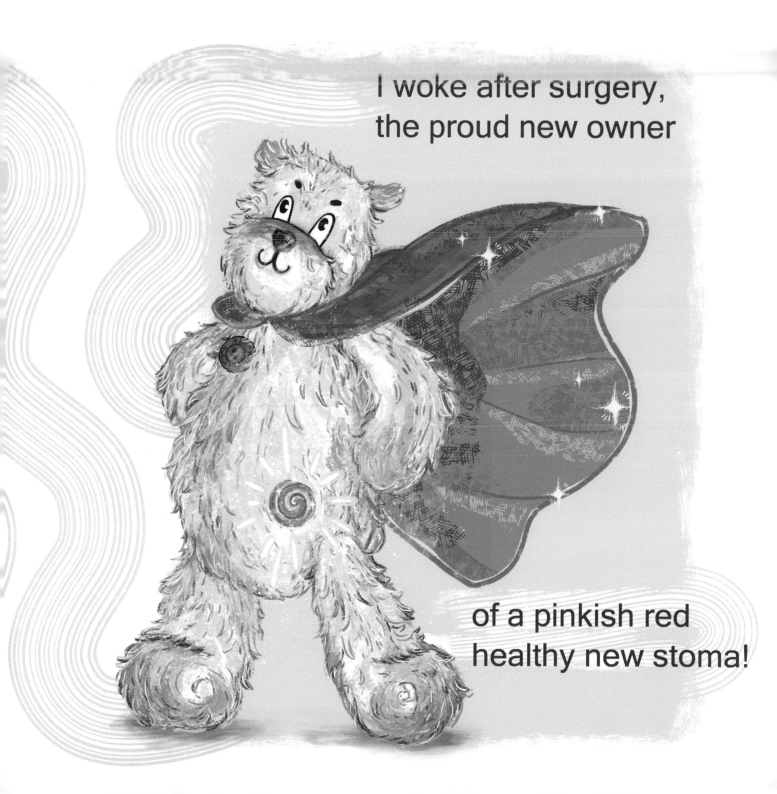

I woke after surgery,
the proud new owner

of a pinkish red
healthy new stoma!

With my bag on my tummy, I set out to find

a friend just like me,
who's cuddly and kind.

I looked near...

and far...

I searched East and West for someone else with a scar, a friend to love best.

Now I've searched up a mountain...

and deep in a cave...

but I've never met anyone...

just quite as brave.

But now I've found you, and I'm sure you'll agree...

...how lovely it is, to find a friend, just like me.

A Bear Named Buttony was launched in Ballater, Aberdeenshire, in May 2015 by a group of friends who wanted to create support for children and young people who have a stoma

---

www.buttonybear.org.uk
info@buttonybear.org.uk
07813 720963

A Bear Named Buttony is a Scottish Charity regulated by the Scottish Charity Regulator (OSCR)

The first issue of this book has been created using funds raised by the Ballater Games Stewards and the Ballater & District Pipe Band.

They held a collection for Buttony at the magnificent Beat Retreat by the Pipe Band on the Church Green after the Games in August 2019 and at the Stewards 'Funcy' Dress Friday.

We are truly humbled by their efforts and indeed all in Ballater, Buttony's home village, who have supported us.

Sometimes you come across an idea that is so simple and obvious that you can't believe nobody thought of it before. Try this one.

Take a standard Teddy Bear, add a small disk on the tummy to look like a stoma and place a bag over it. If I am a child with a stoma this bear now looks like "me". It says my Teddy Bear is different to most other people's bears, but I can love it just as much as they can. What could be more "normalising" to a young child with a stoma or a family whose newborn baby has had to have a stoma as a life-saving procedure? This is what the charity called A Bear Named Buttony does.

I am a Consultant Paediatric Surgeon and I was honoured to be asked to be the Charity's first patron. What drew me to A Bear Named Buttony is that it is unique and is just pure kindness. The Bears, all sponsored by donations, are sent on request to children's surgical units all around the country and the feedback from parents and from staff is both heart-warming and inspiring.

In my job I have had many discussions with parents about their baby, often only a few hours old but with a major abnormality and needing a stoma formation. There is a mixture of shock and horror and real uncertainty about the future. The comfort of knowing that someone else out there has been through this and knows what they are feeling is a massive boost. The Buttony Bear is a symbol of hope at a really dark and difficult time.

But A Bear Named Buttony can't exist without support and a dedicated team of volunteers. These are the cutters and sewers, the stitchers and gluers, the packers and posters who give their skills and not unsubstantial amounts of time to making it work.

I started this with the view that the simple and obvious idea is often the best and parents agree. To finish with a quote from one whose child received a bear: "Stoma life has not been easy, but "E" has gained so much comfort and fun from having Buttony on her journey with her." I think this book will add further comfort and help children realise having a stoma might make them look a bit different but they still have lots of friends in a similar position.

Chris Driver
Consultant Paediatric Surgeon
A Bear Named Buttony Patron and Trustee